"Stop, Miss!"

Whitney Darrow, Jr.

R A N D O M   H O U S E   N E W   Y O R K

Library of Congress Catalog Card Number: 57-10052

Printed in the United States of America by the Murray Printing Company

First
Printing

"Miss! Oh, Miss! For God's sake, stop!"

"Mrs. Minton, there's no such thing as a bad boy. Hostile, perhaps. Aggressive, recalcitrant, destructive, even sadistic. But not __bad__."

"You are charged with disorderly conduct, indecent exposure, and impersonating an officer."

1

"When my husband sees how much I've bought, he'll
throw me right out of the house."

2

"*May I remind you, Haskell, that as Social Director your job is to see that the* <u>guests</u> *are happy?*"

"I don't know whether to take a Benzedrine
and go to the party or a Nembutal and go to bed."

"Now, don't be so modest, Professor. I'm sure
you've got something up your sleeve that will
blow us all to bits."

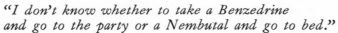

"It's lucky I spent Rud's bonus in advance this year. He didn't get one."

"Boy! What a stinker I'm going to be next year!"

"*For heaven's sake, now, don't sparkle!*"

"There's a very interesting story there. She was voted Mother of the Month up in the States a couple of years ago and given a ten-day, all-expense trip down here."

"*And I promise you, sir, to support her in the manner to which she is accustomed, including all major appliances.*"

"*Oh, Mrs. Williamson!*"

"Well, it was sort of like a cook-out."

*"Well, another day without a cigarette.
That makes fourteen years, seven months,
three weeks, and four days now."*

"Say, just exactly what did you mean by that crack you made when you left this morning?"

"Here's a really sturdy item—built to last for hours."

"*Now, fellows, when the time comes to break camp, let's see if we can't say that nobody has bitten or scratched anybody, and that nobody has been scratched or bitten.*"

"It's one of those new miracle dances."

"Why, this is positively eerie! The bank's figures and mine agree to the exact penny!"

"Look, I told you just ten minutes ago—you've got the wrong address."

"Are you the party who advertised for a married couple?"

"I never thought *that* kind of people were Republicans."

"Well, what's it going to be, Thompson—Hopalong Cassidy or Troop Nine?"

"It's his air of smug self-assurance that I can't stand."

"*We'd like to adopt <u>two</u> children—a baby and a nice, reliable girl of around fifteen or sixteen.*"

"You know damn well that when
I say, 'Stop me if you've heard this,'
I don't mean <u>you</u>."

"I'm sorry the bank can't approve your request
for a loan, Miss Dennis, but I'd be delighted to
tide you over with a little something personally."

"Say, Martha, here's some good picturesque
expressions to use on the summer people."

"If you want to go a little higher, here's
one that also gets the measles."

"Drawing upon my not inconsiderable experience, Andrews, my advice to a young man ambitious of preferment in our calling is to steer clear of two subjects—politics and religion."

"I made up my mind that this year I'd give Aunt Mildred
a dose of her own medicine."

"Damn it, Harlow, aren't you ever going to stop saying, 'Why didn't I think of that'?"

"Going . . .   *Going . . .*   *Gone!"*

"Steinway piano is really tops,
A dandy grand for classical or pops.
Keeps in tune much longer, too.
Steinway piano is the make for you."

"I'm sorry, but we have no openings for announcers. But wait a minute—if you grew a mustache and put on a pair of tortoise-shell glasses, I think we could fit you in as a news analyst."

"_You_ should complain. _I_ had to shell out fifty bucks for an aptitude test and twenty-five more for the damned horn!"

"*I'm afraid we're stymied. He absolutely refuses to accept custody.*"

"*Remember, now, you promised— no television.*"

"*Well, if you broke eighty, why didn't you get home earlier?*"

*"Do you think we __should__ have a second one, Clara?
Remember, we've got to go down those steps."*

*"Look, young man. The cash value of your
$18.75 bond, as we compute it, has not
increased, as of now, beyond the figure of
$18.87 that I gave you this morning."*

"*Mother, I've got wonderful news!*"

"My prediction of last Sunday night that my prediction of a major resignation in the State Department would be denied has proven one-hundred-per-cent correct."

"I paint what I see."

"No, I <u>don't</u> like it, young man. And to tell the truth, I think that suit <u>you're</u> wearing is terrible, too."

"I'm in love with your secretary, Mr. Norton, and I want her for my secretary."

"Don't expect _me_ to believe they didn't know we closed up camp a week ago."

"*What do you want to be when you grow up—drafted?*"

"*That's odd. The salesman seemed comfortable in it.*"

"Surely, Fred, there must be more to life than _this_."

"If I had to choose between a man with brains and a man with brawn, I'd pick the one with the most money."

"... and he also promised me a diesel train with a horn and a red jet bomber and a pair of racing skates and a Doberman pinscher and five pounds of marshmallow fudge."

"First class here, tourist at
the other end of the island."

"But gee, Pop, they say the
doctors all smoke 'em."

"All right, Haskell—sell me."

"Are write-ins permitted?"

1

2

3

4

5

6

"*You might at least have given me a chance to reverse my topcoat.*"

"*She can't remember her cousin's daughter's married name.*"

"*Not yet. I'll tell you when to look.*"

"Say! I saw the <u>exact</u> same thing in 'Life.'"

"*Mr. Swanson, may I present my ideas now, before my Benzedrine wears off?*"

"*And then someday, maybe, the clatter of little feet.*"

"*Hey, Irate Taxpayer, they published your letter!*"

"Will you please stop retracting
your ball-point pen?"

"There, now! You owe me four hundred billion dollars!"

"There! A message of good will for all mankind."

"Someday, my boy, all this will belong to Mr. William Zeckendorf."

"In the words of our great founder, gentlemen, 'Get out and sell!'"

"It isn't the Ds and Fs that bother me. It's that A for effort."

"I can't understand it. The reviews said it was the best cookbook in ten years."

"Same old stuff—boy meets girls, boy loses girls, boy gets girls."

"... Then the phone rang and I answered it and they asked me the name of the song they were playing. I told them. Then they sent me a dozen sport shirts and a red cummerbund and a matched set of alligator airplane luggage and arranged for an all-expense trip to Hollywood, with an evening at Ciro's to be spent in the company of someone called Miss Orange Juice."

"_Now_ I see why everybody thinks they're extinct."

"*Sometimes I get the feeling Henry doesn't need me any more, now that everything in the house is electrified.*"

"But, Harry, you _said_ to bring a friend."

"*What do you mean, 'unescorted'?*"

"*Pop, there's something you didn't tell me about the bees.*"

"Damn it, Harkins, that was _my_ speech you just read!"

"*Look who wants to spend Saturday afternoon with his daddy!*"

"*Let me put it this way. It's five years from now. What am I kicking myself for not having bought?*"

"*Well, folks, it's one of those nights again. Just a crazy, off-the-top-of-your-head unspectacular. Crazy Eddie, here, ate the script, and who knows what's going to happen and probably will? So anyhoo it don't seem like . . .*"

1

"*The makers of Siegfried beer take you to Madison Square Garden for the windup between Mike Mulvane and Rocky Rinaldo.*"

2

"*While the boys are getting set, why don't you get set—with a bottle of Siegfried . . .*"

5

"*Well, that round was in doubt. But there's no doubt about the . . .*"

6

"*. . . best beer for your money . . .*"

9

"*There's the bell ending the ninth. Time for a breather, and that means . . .*"

10

"*. . . the lager that likes you.*"

3

"...rich as velvet, smooth as silk..."

4

"Bell for the third coming up. Just time to latch onto another bottle of that beer no other beer can lay a glove on."

7

"...and while you're out there, make sure you've got enough blond beauties on ice."

8

"...looks like Mulvane's losing his head. You keep one on that glass of yours."

11

"Don't forget our six-can Handipak, and the money-saving case of twenty-four..."

12

"It's Rinaldo, folks, by a decision! And here's a winner by a decision, too —Siegfried beer, First for Thirst!!"

"Notice, class, how Angela circles, always keeping the desk between them . . ."

"I don't mind fire and brimstone on Fifth Avenue, but on the Cape! Well, really!"

"You can't tell. He may have won a bundle on a quiz show."

"I'm _glad_ I didn't win anything. That
gardener of mine would have expected a raise."

"... and remember, the Black Vulture
knows if bad little boys and girls neglect
to remind their mothers when it's time
to get a new case of Rhubarbola."

"We wonder if you'd care to
come to the funeral of our turtle."

"... the stock market moved irregularly lower yesterday in a day of dull trading. Rails and industrials held steady. Brazilian bonds showed a marked flurry in the final hours of trading. Municipal issues were generally ..."

"Look, Joe, I'm calling that wind last night a terrific gale, and I don't want you crossing me up in *your* book."

"Please pardon me, but I represent the Eastern Burglar Alarm Company, and I just wanted to demonstrate how vulnerable you are."

"My first husband and I tried separate vacations. Matter of fact, that's when I met my present husband."

"...a beer that's right...a sheer delight... day or night...kite...bright...try it tonight"

"You're fired! You, Preston, that is."

"*Did I understand you to say this is your autobiography?*"

"*Here's our special de-luxe gift combination—one hundred per cent rag paper, clear-vision thumb index, genuine leather binding, and white-wall tires.*"

"And upon the completion of your course you will be driven to your home by a trusted employee, since it will no longer be safe for you to go about the streets alone."

"Well, it happened this way. I was out prospecting for uranium when suddenly my Geiger counter started clicking, and there, coming toward me up the road, was the girl who was to become your mother, wearing a white dress, a straw hat, and a radium-dial wristwatch."

"Trouble is, Doc, I feel inferior to people I _know_ I'm superior to."

"I don't care what Leonard Hall and all those others say. I think you'd make a _perfect_ President."

"See! I told you the schedule said two days in Nassau,
three in Maracaibo, and <u>one</u> day here."

"Well, it's a beginning, at least."

1

2

3

4

5

6

Whitney Darrow, Jr.

"*Well, I finally saw that psychiatrist you've been pestering me about, and I give you three guesses who's at the root of all my trouble.*"

"It still has a few bugs in it."

"Duz, Pep, Crax, Lux, Kix, Spam, Spic,
Spry, and a container of milk."

"Oh, __morally__ bankrupt. For a moment, I was afraid you meant financially."

1

2

3

4

5

"Henry, I've fallen in love with our marriage counsellor."

"You're certainly going to look silly if it isn't uranium."

*"Watch your step with this one.
He writes letters."*

*"I had a wonderful acceptance speech all
ready. I don't suppose you fellows would
care to hear it?"*

"Oh dear! My figure has gone out of style again."

"The lignatae diurniti mothola be hanged, Phyllis. It's _you_ I want."

"I'm beginning to notice girls, Pop. Don't you think you ought to boost my allowance?"

"But the doctor _ordered_ me to take those
three weeks at Hot Springs."

"It's delicious. What happened?"

"For heaven's sake, Fullerton, relax and enjoy yourself. What the Rockefeller Foundation doesn't know won't hurt them."

"Disney will <u>love</u> this—that is, if Harrison comes out on top."

"Great layout. Like the whole campaign.
Shoot the works. By the way, what the hell _is_ Z9?"

". . . You're ready to begin after you've washed
your face with soap and water in the ordinary way.
You apply your shaving cream to the brush and
lather the face liberally, working the lather in
thoroughly with the fingertips . . ."

"Well, how was 'The Late Late Show'?"

"This one would really make
him blow his top."

"Good heavens, Emma! I thought this was you."

"*I've got group insurance, so don't pull any punches.*"

"*Because he was naughty, dear.*"

*"I have never stooped, my friends, nor will I now stoop, to the kind of
vicious falsehoods, mud-slinging, and personal vilification indulged
in by my opponent and his Commie pals."*

"*Darling! I had no idea you were such a good credit risk.*"

"*I don't want to confuse you with a lot of medical jargon. Let's put it this way—it'll cost you five hundred dollars.*"

"*I think you'll find that we've got that kleptomania under control, Mrs. Barclay, but if you should have a little relapse, would you mind picking up a nice desk clock for me?*"

"*Well, if you ask me, they're not ready for statehood!*"

"Now, isn't this better than paying those peak-of-the-season rates?"

"After all, Mr. Jackson, we do require our students to have <u>some</u> degree of aptitude."

"Now, don't just _say_ you like it."

"While you're at it, ask her what the middle-class Parisian housewife whose husband can barely keep his head above water is wearing this year."

"Oh, and speaking of Mother, just send her the bills. She takes care of all those things."

"Want to hear me count to five hundred by fives?"

"He writes the cleverest notes! 'To the sweetest, most adorable, most beautiful, charming, and intelligent girl in all the world.'"

"I'd like to see one of those Russians try to get friendly with _me_!"

"I'm afraid we'll have to close down your show, Pearson. We had no idea your work was so controversial."

"For God's sake, Martha!"

"Remember, now, we're not in business for our health."

"Now, let's see. Linda, how many teeth do you have?"

"*Just follow this diet, and we'll have you back in
that M.G. within a month.*"

"It certainly makes one realize how insignificant you are."

"*Young man, you go right back to Brockbank, Brockbank, Brockbank, and Brockbank and tell them to send me a Brockbank.*"

"Well, I did and I didn't. I was helping an old lady across the street, but she was sideswiped by a taxicab."

"Now, here's the way it is. We're the good guys and they're the bad guys. We give you the ball. You run with it from here down to there. The bad guys will try to stop you. O.K. so far?"

"Would you mind telling my husband dinner is ready?"

"Really, old man, I didn't mean it was a __bad__ novel. Just a little weak in spots!"

"By golly, I think it __is__ getting bigger."

"Hey, Combs! Where the hell do you think you're going?"

"No, no, let them lay, Jones, let them _lay_!"

"Dad, can I have the carpet tonight?"

"Just a minute, Martha. Haven't you forgotten something?"

"*That's the kind of man I'm going to marry.*"

"*What do you mean you have nothing to do? Go tie some knots. Start a fire. Weave a basket. Collect something.*"

"*We're pleased with the way you're taking hold here, Nesbitt, and you'll be glad to know that as of the first of the month we're giving you a desk nearer the windows.*"

"*The poor thing got frostbite rummaging in her deep freeze.*"

"Mebbe 'tis, mebbe 'tisn't. Your name Spalding?"

"*Can't that kid ever stay home? When I was his age, you didn't catch me gallivanting around night after night to every damned fertility rite on the island.*"

"Dad, you _promised!_"

"Are you sure this is the Westport train?
I don't see any Westport faces."

"Ever have the feeling you're
not being followed?"

"*But I want you to know, Albert, that if I were going to marry someone like you, it would certainly be you.*"

"*I'm not good enough for you, Helen.*"

"*And, of course, we don't want to offend any <u>majority</u> groups, either.*"

"*Mr. Bates, you mean this Little Theatre group of yours is just you and me?*"

"I'm cancelling my appointments for the next
three days, Mrs. Belden—I'm having the couch done over."

1

2

"It isn't that I don't think you're funny, Harvey, and it isn't that the sponsor or the network doesn't think you're funny. It's just that millions and millions of people all over America don't think you're funny."

"Pardon me, but I thought you might like to know that from up here you stick out like a sore thumb."

"Long time no see."

"When you say you hate your species, Ronald, do you mean __everyone__?"

"Marge, is it yellow or gray you look like hell in?"